£1.50

. . . PRIZE . . .

AWARDED TO

David Henderson, for Merit in

P7b of St. Monance School.

July 1964

J. F. Boyle

MAN AGAINST MUTINY

The Story of Vice-Admiral William Bligh

A man of courage and action, always willing to stand doggedly by what he thought was right.

MAN AGAINST MUTINY

The Story of Vice-Admiral William Bligh

JOYCE NICHOLSON

LUTTERWORTH PRESS

LONDON

First published 1961

COPYRIGHT © 1961 LUTTERWORTH PRESS

PRINTED IN GREAT BRITAIN BY
NORTHUMBERLAND PRESS LIMITED
GATESHEAD ON TYNE

CONTENTS

Route of the *Bounty*

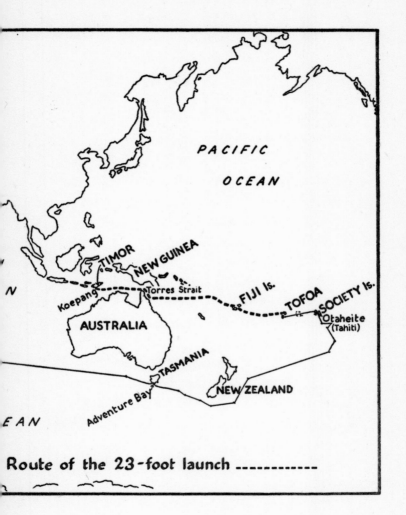

Route of the 23-foot launch ------------

" COME on," whispered Fletcher Christian. "Come on. What are you waiting for? We'll never get a better chance."

He looked round at the excited faces of the small group gathered about him. They were rough, coarse faces, belonging to men who had seen only the hardest things in life, born and bred in the slums of England, ill-educated, knowing nothing but poverty, and forced by this poverty into the Navy, one of the hardest lives imaginable.

"You'll never get a better chance," urged Christian again. "Let's take the ship now. And then back to Otaheite! "

"That's what I say," muttered Thomas Burkitt. "The old man's asleep in 'is bunk. An' the door wide open! " He laughed roughly. "Thinks 'e can trust us, 'e does."

"An' both them fine young gentlemen," added Matthew Quintal scornfully, "that calls themselves midshipmen—both asleep on their watch. C'mon, I'm all for it."

"But say we get caught," muttered Mills. "Yer know what that'll mean."

"How can we be caught?" asked Christian. "The ship's at our mercy. As Quintal here says, young Hallet is asleep on the arms chest."

"Yeah," muttered Quintal. "We'll nab 'im quickly enough. Get the arms, and then we're set. I'm with yer, Christian."

"They'll send another ship out from England after us," objected Mills again. "You see if they don't."

"They'll never catch us," replied Christian confidently. "I promise you that. We'll get straight back to Otaheite, get the girls and some of the men, and find another island. Think of it, men! To spend the rest of your life on an island like Otaheite, and never to see England again."

As this small group of men plotted, the sea lay around them in perfect peace. The first glimmer of light was brightening the horizon of a still, tropical sea, and the small ship *Bounty* moved slowly on, her sails spread to catch every breath of wind. She was a ship of only two hundred and fifteen tons, ninety-one feet long and twenty-four feet wide, with a mere forty-five men aboard, and yet she had sailed nearly around the world.

From England to Cape Horn in South America she had been, and then, driven back by storms, to the Cape of Good Hope in South Africa, and from there across the Antarctic Ocean, below the unknown continent of New Holland, or Australia, to reach her destination, the island of Otaheite in the South Seas.

She had stayed at Otaheite for six months and was now bound once more for the Cape of Good Hope and then for the West Indies and back to England.

In his cabin below decks, the Captain of the *Bounty* slept soundly. He lay in his night shirt, with the door of his cabin wide open, to catch any cool air that might find its way below decks, and to be easily called by the crew. He slept with a clear conscience, and the knowledge that he had done his duty well. He had brought his tiny boat and small band of men right around the world, fifteen months from England, without any illness. He had taken on board at Otaheite one thousand and fifteen breadfruit plants, all in flourishing condition. These were to be taken to St. Vincent and Jamaica, to feed the negro slaves that worked on British plantations. Yes, Lieutenant William Bligh, Captain of the *Bounty*, slept at peace with the world.

If Bligh were at peace, however, there were several members of his crew who were not. Led by the handsome young Mate, Fletcher Christian, they were plotting to capture the boat. Christian had just taken over the morning watch, and with him were the roughest men in the crew, men who faced the long, wearisome journey home and then an England of slums and poverty. As for Christian, his one wish was to return to Otaheite, where he had fallen in love with a beautiful Tahitian girl, soon to become the mother of his child.

How easy it was for Christian to stir up these malcontents to the idea of mutiny. And how easily the way lay open for them. The Captain was asleep with his door open. The two young midshipmen on watch were both asleep, Thomas Hayward on deck, and John Hallett stretched out on the arms chest he was supposed to be guarding, and Fletcher Christian, who should have been in charge, was the leader of the revolt.

He moved among the men, stirring up their discontent, their hatred of all authority. With mutterings and curses and groans they bemoaned their fate, thinking with dread of the long journey home, the cold, the discipline, the short rations. In contrast, there was the island they had just left, where it was always warm, there was always plenty to eat, there was no need to work, and there were beautiful girls awaiting them.

Suddenly they made the decision. Why shouldn't they take the boat and return to the island? They hated the Navy, they hated all officers. No love for their country or the sea had made them join the Navy. They were pressganged, dragged from wharves and slums, or they had signed up because it was the only way they could make a living.

There were about twelve of them altogether, and others asleep that they knew they could rely on. Christian gave his final hurried orders, and then they surged down the companionway. John Hallett was hauled roughly off the arms chest, and still half asleep was thrust up on deck to join Hayward.

Quickly, the mutineers armed themselves with muskets from the arms chest, and two men went on deck to stand guard over the young midshipmen.

"Sumner and Quintal," growled Christian softly, "you keep guard over Fryer and Peckover. See the scoundrels don't interfere." John Fryer, the Master of the ship, and William Peckover, the gunner, were both asleep in their cabins.

"And the rest of you, come with me," concluded Christian, "and we'll see the end of our friend, Mr. Bligh."

"No killin'," muttered one of the mutineers, "yer mind, yer promised no killin'."

"Oh, stow it," muttered another. "Run the

'ole lot of 'em through, that's what I'd do. All they're good for."

Then they were at the open door of Bligh's cabin. Christian, Churchill, Burkett and Mills crowded in, and Christian roughly hauled the sleeping captain from his bunk.

"One word from you, Mr. Bligh," he shouted, " and you're a dead man."

Immediately there was uproar. If the young midshipmen, Hallett and Hayward, had taken their arrest with amazement and no resistance, not so their Captain.

"What's this? What's this?" he shouted, struggling with all his strength. "Lay your hands off me. You dastardly scoundrels, you scum of the earth! How dare you attack me!"

Bligh's voice rang through the ship. "Mutiny!" he shouted. "Mr. Fryer! Mr. Peckover!" There were confused shouts from everywhere now, but it was to no avail. What could Bligh do against four men in the cabin, all armed, and several more standing outside? Two men held his arms behind him and Christian tied his wrists with a cord. Then, holding the cord, they thrust Bligh in front of them, up the companionway, on to the deck, continuously threatening him with death, if he uttered another word.

"So help me, Mr. Bligh, I'll run you through with this bayonet," shouted Christian. "Shut your mouth!"

But nothing would silence Bligh. "Run me through, if you like, you ungrateful coward. You won't silence me." He pleaded with some of the mutineers to change their minds. He continued to call for help. Then he turned to Christian to plead with him.

"Unhand me, Christian," he said. "What can you mean by this? Why have you turned on me? You, who I've treated as a son?" He spoke the truth, too. This was the third time Christian had sailed under his command, and always he had shown him special favours, for he was a cousin of his wife.

But Christian would not meet his commander's eyes. "You don't understand, Mr. Bligh," was all he could mutter. "You don't know what I've been through this last fortnight," Then he turned on Bligh again, pointing the bayonet at Bligh's throat.

Still Bligh kept on calling to other members of the crew. Helpless himself, with his hands held behind him, and with several armed men standing nearby, he could do nothing but beg others to act. He appealed again to some of the mutineers to change their minds. To those officers on deck he appealed for action. But there were too few of them, and the mutineers guarded the hatchways with muskets, keeping the others below.

Meanwhile, confusion reigned everywhere.

"What's happening? What's happening?" asked Purcell, the carpenter. He was roughly told that Mr. Bligh, Mr. Hayward, Mr. Hallett, and Mr. Samuels were to be put in the cutter and set adrift.

"But the cutter's leaking," exclaimed William Cole, the boatswain. "It wouldn't last a moment. That'd be sheer murder."

"Shut your mouth, or you're dead this moment," growled one of the mutineers.

By this time the cutter was lowered, with Michael Byrne, the blind fiddler, in it. Though quite useless as a sailor, Byrne had been taken by Bligh so that his men would have music and dancing during the long voyage.

"You can't use the cutter," complained others. "Can't you see it's leaking."

"Give them the launch then," shouted someone.

"Yes, give the wretches the launch."

There were other reasons now for changing from the tiny cutter to the launch. It had quickly been seen by the ringleaders of the mutiny that more than half the crew were against them. They could guard them now where the mutineers were armed and the others helpless, but what would happen later on? When the ship was moving, when the mutineers were asleep, it would be dangerous to have half the crew plotting to take back the ship.

"Yes," growled Christian. "Give them the launch, and put all those against us in it. We want no traitors on this ship."

So Cole, with the help of others, lowered the launch: and Hayward, Hallett, and Mr. Samuel were ordered into it. Samuel, Bligh's clerk, had, in the meantime, collected Bligh's journals, his commission, a few other ship's papers, a quadrant and a compass. But he was forbidden to take the time-keeper, sextant, or a box in which Bligh kept his surveys, drawings, and maps, collected over the previous fifteen years, and containing his notes made during that time. These were lost with the *Bounty*, and as Bligh had specialized in the art of mapping and survey, this was a grievous loss to him

and the Navy. Samuel also collected some of
Bligh's clothes and a little food.

Still there was confusion. The mutineers
argued, with oaths and curses, about who should
and should not go into the launch. When it came
to William Purcell, the carpenter, some wanted to
keep him.

"We'll need the wretch on the *Bounty*," growled
one mutineer.

"No," argued another, " 'e'll only make trouble.
Let 'im go. Keep the carpenter's mates."

But the carpenter's mates, Norman and
McIntosh, did not want to stay on the *Bounty*.

"We've had no part in the mutiny," they cried.
"We want to go with Mr. Bligh."

"Shut yer mouth," roared William McKoy.
"Yer stayin' with us."

By this time the launch was filling up. Christian
ordered that the master, the quartermasters, the
sailmaker, the surgeon, the botanist and the mates
be now allowed on deck, and they all climbed down
into the launch, amid much jeering and cursing
from the mutineers. Gradually the small boat
began to sink low in the water. This caused great
amusement among some of the mutineers.

"Put a few more in," they laughed, "then she'll
sink to the bottom."

Meanwhile, those already in the launch were
calling out for food and water to be given to them,
and the carpenter was begging to be allowed to
take his tool chest. The boatswain, with help from
others, managed to get some sails, twine, rope,
grapnel, and a small cask of water into the boat.
Then the gunner and the cooks and the butcher

were forced down into the launch, but the armourer, Coleman, in spite of his pleading that he had a wife and children at home, was not allowed to go. Bligh, meanwhile, was still trying to talk sense into Christian and the mutineers. Part of the time he was threatening them, the other part trying to reason with them, but Christian merely shouted and scowled at him, saying he would kill him. Finally he felt there were enough men in the launch.

"Come, Captain Bligh," he ordered. "Your officers and men are now in the boat, and you must go with them. Make any resistance, and you'll be instantly put to death."

The other mutineers were also growing tired of the whole business.

"Shut 'im up," they shouted, and "Cast 'im off," "Let's get back to Otaheite," and "Run 'em all through."

So Bligh too was forced into the boat. He made one last effort.

"Christian," he called, "at least give us some arms. We shall be at the mercy of the natives."

One of the mutineers guffawed at this. "But you're such a friend o' the natives, Mr. Bligh. You don't need no arms."

Bligh had prided himself on his friendship and understanding with the natives at Otaheite, and had allowed none of the crew to do them any harm. The worst elements in the crew had not liked this, and were now getting their revenge. Others, however, had kinder hearts and felt some pity for the men in the overladen launch, and, at the last moment, a few cutlasses were handed down, and a

B

few pieces of pork and a little more bread was thrown into the boat.

Finally, it was set adrift, nineteen men in a twenty-three-foot launch. The mutineers on the *Bounty* roared down abuse, insults and jibes, except for Michael Byrne, the blind fiddler, who was crying, and the carpenter's mates and the armourer, who called out desperately, reminding Bligh and the others in the launch that they had wanted to come too, and had no part in the mutiny.

As the gap between the tiny launch and the *Bounty* widened, shouts of "HURRAH FOR OTA-HEITE" from the larger ship could be heard coming across the waters.

A S the *Bounty* sailed away, William Bligh gazed at the bewildered men gathered so closely around him. Some were silent with dismay, others were arguing about what had caused the mutiny.

"They wanted to get back to Otaheite, that's all," said Cole bluntly. "Too much soft living, they've all had. That's the trouble."

"Have any of you heard or seen any signs of a plot?" asked Bligh, as he struggled into some of the clothes Samuel had brought for him. No one had heard anything. The whole thing had completely surprised them all.

"We'd have heard, if they'd been plotting it," said Ledward, the surgeon. "Someone would have heard. They must have decided all of a sudden."

"Spurred on by that Fletcher Christian," added Cole. "He's been wanting to get back to the island ever since we left it."

Bligh frowned. "Christian, Christian," he moaned. "I can't bear to think of him. You think he was the leader?"

"Well, he was in charge of them, wasn't he? And it was his watch, wasn't it?"

"And you remember," said Purcell, "we found him trying to make a raft, about a week ago. He said he was going to jump overboard and go back to that girl of his."

"What's that? What's that?" roared Bligh. "No one mentioned it to me."

19

"We thought nothing more about it," replied Cole. "We thought it was just the foolishness of a young man. He is a young fool, you know, sir. We talked him out of it, and forgot all about it."

"I can't believe it," replied Bligh slowly. "Fletcher Christian! I can't believe it." There had often been words between them, it was true, and he had had to berate the young man for his carelessness, but it had all been for his own good. That he should do this to him! Suddenly Bligh shook his head, as though to get rid of these thoughts. He sat up straight, and looked at the men. There were important things to do. Stunned though he was at what had just happened, angry though he was at the way he had been handled, the main thing was to restore some order to the small crowded launch, and to plan the best way to save his men. Bligh was in command again.

He counted those on board. Nineteen men, and hardly a good seaman among them! Cooks, he thought to himself, and a butcher, a sailmaker, a carpenter, a botanist, a clerk! Nearly all the sailors were on board the *Bounty*. Any lesser man would have quailed at the mere idea of getting nineteen such men home in a twenty-three-foot launch. There was scarcely room for them to all sit up comfortably. How could they possibly survive?

But the whole of Bligh's life had been a battle, a struggle for success, and to him, this was one more obstacle to overcome. It was at once clear to him that the sternest discipline and control would be necessary, and that food would be the greatest problem.

"Now listen, men," he said sternly, "what food is there? Every bit of food must be carefully saved and shared. I won't have anyone keeping things for himself," he added bluntly. "D'you understand that?"

"Here's some pork," said William Cole.

"And there's some bread here," said others, unwillingly parting with food they were holding.

"And some rum and wine."

"Come on. Come on," said Bligh impatiently. "Hurry up. Hand everything along to me at once. At once, d'you hear, Mr. Purcell!"

Bligh was never a man to choose his words carefully. He spoke bluntly and often tactlessly, not realizing the way his words sometimes affected others. His first thought was always for the welfare of his men, and he was blunt and short because he knew what was best for them and he had no intention of arguing about it. If left to themselves, he knew they would have eaten the food in a few days.

So the food, water and wine were passed along until everything was collected in front of Bligh. He and Mr. Samuel sorted it out, and there it lay, a sorry heap indeed.

"And that's all there is," said Bligh shortly. "You can all see for yourself. So I'll have no argument about it. 150 pounds of bread, sixteen pieces of pork. Each weighs about two pounds, I think. Six quarts of rum, six bottles of wine, twenty eight gallons of water, and four empty barrecoes. So," he smiled, as he added drily, "we'll at least have something to drink out of. But the food," he continued, "must be made to last. Don't forget it's a long way home."

Well, thought young Thomas Hayward, you have to give it to the old man. He's not going to let us die tomorrow. And others in the launch felt the same. Hopelessness began to give way to optimism. Domineering though he was, their Captain was not just thinking of today or tomorrow, but of when they reached home again. It is surely a great tribute to Bligh that he could see so far ahead, for from the very first moment, and in face of much opposition, he started rationing the food.

"And now," he continued, "for further plans. First we must try and get more food. We won't touch our stores unless absolutely necessary. D'you all hear that?" he asked, looking around fiercely. The others all nodded.

"We'll sail for Tofoa," he continued. "It's quite near and we'll see what we can get from the natives. Then we'll try Tongataboo, I think, and see if King Paulaho will help us build a bigger boat."

Under his instructions, they managed to erect a sail and by nightfall reached Tofoa. But rough seas stopped them from landing, and they spent the night in the boat. Even at this early stage Bligh would allow them no food, but gave each man half a pint of grog, and, as he wrote in his log, each then "took to his rest as well as our unhappy situation would allow."

In the morning they still could find no good place to land, but some of the men got ashore by struggling through the surf. However, only a few quarts of water and about twenty coconuts were found. So for dinner that day each man was given "a morsel of bread and a glass of wine", wrote Bligh in his log, and for supper "each man was served a coconut".

Again on the following morning they were unable to find a good landing place. The best they could do was to anchor the boat offshore, in a small cove, where steep cliffs had to be climbed to get to the land above. This time Bligh went with a party to look for food. A few plantains and some water were found, and for dinner Bligh gave about an ounce of pork and two plantains to each, with half a glass of wine. During the afternoon they found a cave at the head of the cove, and that night built a fire in front of it, so that Bligh and some of the crew were able to spend the night there, giving the men left in the boat more room to sleep.

"The people who remained by the boat," wrote Bligh in his log, "I had directed to look for fish or what they could pick up about the rocks, but nothing eatable could be found, so that upon the whole we considered ourselves on as miserable a spot of land as could well be imagined." For supper that night, he allowed the men each one boiled plantain and a quarter of a pint of grog. So ended the third day of a fruitless search for food. The next two days were to bring tragedy.

While looking for food, Bligh had been hoping to meet some natives, as from these in the past they had always been able to get things to eat. Pigs were often brought along, in addition to breadfruit and coconuts. On the next day, natives did begin to appear, about thirty altogether. At first they were very friendly, and brought breadfruit, plantains, and water. They chattered continuously, and, as usual, wanted to touch and finger the boat.

"Where big ship?" they asked.

As he had expected this question, Bligh had already discussed it with his men. He felt it was useless to say the ship was coming to join them, as the natives could see from the hills that it was nowhere in sight. It was decided to say it had been wrecked, and the men in the launch saved. Everyone told the same story, and the natives seem satisfied, but very surprised. All that day the natives kept coming and going, but brought very little food, and there was no chief among them with whom Bligh could speak. He began to feel worried.

"We'll never get enough here," he said to Fryer, the Master, "to stock us for a long voyage. In the meantime, we must keep the same rations for each meal."

Next day he sent out another party to look for water and more food, and suddenly the natives began to gather around in larger numbers. Bligh began to worry again, but when two Chiefs appeared among them, Eefow and Nageete, he felt more hopeful. He gave them each an old shirt and a knife, and found they had seen him before and also remembered Captain Cook. His mind was not completely at rest, however, because although they appeared friendly, they kept asking about the ship.

Then suddenly there was a change in the atmosphere. The numbers of the natives were increasing all the time, and they began to crowd around. Perhaps they finally decided that these white men really were here without a big ship and without any firearms. Some started knocking stones together, which Bligh knew was the sign for an attack. Some started to haul the boat into the shore. Bligh realized the need for some action, and he brandished a cutlass at them. They left the boat alone for the time being, and quietened down a little, but Bligh and his men knew that all was not well.

Gradually a feeling of dread and presentiment began to steal over them. They looked around at the hundreds of natives now standing in hostile groups, looking at them, lining the beach, slowly knocking stones together. How different, thought Bligh, their attitude was towards a defenceless small group of white men without a ship or muskets for protection. The natives knew only too well the power of the dreaded firesticks.

At no time was Bligh's courage greater than during this day of terror. Had he given way to panic, and rushed for the boat, or had he loosened his hold on his men, so that they rushed for the boat, the natives would have leapt on them as a man and clubbed and speared them to death.

But Bligh did none of these things. He went on bargaining with the natives for the small amounts of food they were bringing in. He spoke cheerfully to the Chiefs and asked them to stop the men touching the boat. Just then the foraging party returned.

" Any luck? " he asked cheerfully. But the party

could show only three gallons of water for their morning's search.

"Put them in the boat," ordered Bligh.

Some of the men urged Bligh to leave. But he remained cheerful and firm.

"No," he said sharply, "if we leave now we shall have to fight our way out. We must wait until night, we shall have more chance in the dark. Also," he added, "we can pretend then that we are going to the boat to sleep."

He ordered everyone to go on behaving as naturally as possible, and to get what supplies they could slowly into the boat. He then calmly ordered dinner for everyone, a coconut and a breadfruit for each person, and some also to the Chiefs, with whom he continued to talk and laugh.

No one, however, was deceived. There was a quietness and watchfulness everywhere, and as the afternoon wore on, Bligh and his men began to get their things down from the cave, where they had spent the night, into the boat. More and more natives arrived, and then, late in the afternoon, they started building fires.

"They're going to stay the night all right," Bligh murmured to David Nelson, the botanist. "I'm quite sure we'll be attacked as soon as we start getting into the boat."

Nelson and the others agreed.

"Go down and tell Fryer that as soon as he sees us coming down the beach, to keep the boat close into the shore," he ordered. "The quicker we can get in the more chance we'll have."

Nelson went down casually to give Fryer the message. Then, just as the sun was setting, and the trees and rocks were throwing long shadows across the sand, Bligh told those still with him, near the cave, to pick up the last of their goods, and move slowly towards the boat.

Immediately the Chiefs gathered around.

"You stay in cave tonight?" asked Nageete.

"No, Nageete," replied Bligh smiling and moving slowly down the beach. "I never sleep out of my boat. But don't worry, we'll see you again in the morning. In the morning we'll trade with you again. We'll stay still the sea gets calmer, and then we'll all go, just as we said, to see Poulaho at Tongataboo."

While he was speaking Bligh kept on moving down the beach, with his men before him. But the tension was increasing and the knocking of stones growing louder. Suddenly Eefow walked quickly away.

"You not sleep on shore?" he shouted. "Then *mattie*."

The throbbing in Bligh's heart became almost unbearable. *Mattie*, he knew, meant "kill," but still he showed no sign of his fear. By now only two or three things were left to be put in the boat, so he took the other chief, Nageete, by the arm, and drew him down the beach with him.

"Everyone," he wrote in his log, was "in a silent kind of horror." Still holding Nageete, Bligh drew near to the boat. "It was my determination," he wrote later, "if the natives began to attack, to kill him for his treacherous behaviour." Nageete kept on urging Bligh to stay, but by now all were on board except Bligh, and the native Chief could see that he too was going. He must have decided that if he did not act at once, it would be too late. He suddenly broke away and ran up the beach, calling to the gathered natives to attack.

Bligh jumped on board, and, just for a moment, it looked as if all would be all right. Then disaster struck. Just as Bligh was climbing on board, one of the men realized that the stern rope had not been cast off, and he jumped over the side and ran up the beach to undo it.

Everyone in the boat shouted to him to come back, but it was too late. The natives, seeing their larger prey escaping, leapt on this lonely, brave man, and in five seconds he was clubbed and stoned to death. At the same time, other natives started hauling on the rope to pull the boat back to shore, and the rest, hundreds of them, started throwing stones at the eighteen men left in the launch.

Once again, Bligh acted to save the day.

" My knife," he gasped, and pulling a knife out of his pocket he cut the rope. "And now ROW," he shouted. But the men did not need to be told. Everyone who could, grabbed an oar and desperately began to row away. A shower of stones followed them, striking and hurting everyone in the boat. Then, to their horror, several of the natives loaded their canoes with stones and paddled after them.

"They're gaining on us," cried Fryer in terror. "We are gone."

"Throw over some of the clothes," roared Bligh. "Quickly, men! Some of the clothes."

Shirts, pants and hats went overboard, and the ruse proved successful. The natives, always curious, stopped to pick up the clothes, and just at that moment darkness fell over the sea. The men could not believe they were really safe at last, and went on rowing desperately, but this time they finally got away.

"They at last quitted us," wrote Bligh in his log. "to reflect on our unhappy situation. The poor man I lost was called John Norton. This was his second voyage with me as a Quarter Master, and his worthy character made me feel his loss very severely."

So once again the launch was on the ocean, this time with only eighteen men aboard, but no more provisions than five days earlier.

THE men rowed until their arms and backs and legs could stand no more, and then others took over from them. They were terrified by what had happened on the island. During the six months spent at Otaheite they had never seen the natives in an ugly mood. For Bligh it was different. He had seen the natives kill Captain Cook, and he had seen other native attacks. He knew they had taken a risk in landing at Tofoa, but had felt it was necessary to try and get more food.

When they were well away from the island, he ordered the men to stop rowing, and they hoisted the sails. His mind had been busy with the problem of what they should do next. Should they risk landing on another island? The amount of food they had was ridiculously small; but was the risk of death by natives greater?

He was not left long to think. As soon as the sails were hoisted and the men could rest, they examined the injuries they had received from the stones thrown at them. Everyone had lumps and bruises and broken skin. Some were still shaking with fright. Others were still sickened at the memory of what had happened to John Norton.

Every single member of the crew begged Bligh not to land on any more islands.

"Let's stay in the boat, sir," said William Cole, "at least we're safe from natives here."

"Safe, man?" warned Bligh. "Safe from

natives, you might be. But what about hunger? And thirst? And storms? And the ocean? Thousands of miles of unknown sea, there are, between us and the nearest settlement. What do you say to that?"

"But you know the sea, sir," argued David Nelson, the botanist. "You can find your way on any ocean. Surely it's better the sea you know than natives that can turn on us like that," and he pointed back to the land they had just left behind them.

Everyone said the same. Bligh pointed out that the nearest white settlement he knew of was at Timor, where he believed a few Dutch people lived. To reach this they would have to travel nearly four thousand miles, across the Pacific ocean, through the dangerous reefs that ran down the coast of New Holland, through the treacherous Endeavour Straits between New Holland and New Guinea, and then to Timor.

Still the men begged him to set a course for home.

"All right," he agreed at last, "but you'll have to agree to strict rations. An ounce of bread and a quarter of a pint of water a day is about all there'll be. Can you do it? Will you promise faithfully to stick by it? For I'll not let the food be eaten in the first few days. There'll be no more and I'll have no complaining," he concluded bluntly.

The men were willing to promise anything.

"And so," wrote Bligh in his log, "after examining what our real stock of provisions was, and recommending this as a sacred promise forever to their memory, we bore away across a sea where the navigation is dangerous and but little known, and in a small boat, twenty-three feet long from stem to stern, deep loaded with eighteen souls, without a single map, and nothing but my own recollection and general knowledge of the situation of places, assisted by an old book of latitude and longitude to guide me. I was happy, however, to see that everyone seemed better satisfied with our situation than myself."

At that moment, no doubt, the men had complete faith in Bligh being able to get them anywhere. They knew he was a wonderful sailor. Their faith was justified, but it was not only his knowledge of the sea that saved them. It was also the iron control he kept over the men and the rations.

So the decision was made. Bligh then asked the men, crowded in the small boat, to pray, and one can imagine the thankfulness that welled up in the most hardened hearts when they thought of the danger they had just escaped. "We returned thanks to God," Bligh wrote in his log, "for our miraculous preservation, and, fully confident of His gracious support, I found my mind more at ease . . ."

He then divided the men into watches, and they settled down, as best they could, for the night.

Thus began what is still the most amazing sea voyage that has ever occurred. No other famous long sea voyage in a small craft quite compares with it, both because of the lack of preparedness and the number of men crowded in the small launch.

Next morning the organization of the boat began in earnest. Their provision were checked again and were now 150 pounds of bread, 28 gallons of water, 20 pounds of pork, three bottles of wine and five quarts of rum. A few coconuts and breadfruit in the bottom of the boat had been trampled on and some of the pork had also disappeared in the confusion of the escape. As the bread was in bags, and in danger of getting wet, a wooden chest that Purcell had for his clothes, and another one in which he kept his tools, were taken to keep the food in, and the tools were carefully placed in the bottom of the boat.

Several of the men had also managed to bring away quite a few clothes with them, but to make as much room as possible, Bligh ordered that only two suits should be kept for each person. The rest was thrown overboard, with some rope and spare sails.

The very first morning their troubles began. A violent storm hit the boat, and every few moments waves came right over the men. Everyone had to start bailing desperately, and it was only a miracle that they kept afloat. By dinner-time, every man was drenched and miserably cold. Some of them could hardly believe their eyes, when Bligh began rationing out their dinner, a teaspoonful of rum for each person, and a quarter of a breadfruit.

"How can you expect us to work on that amount of food," grumbled Lamb, the butcher. "The bailing's near killing us. Give us some more at least for today, sir." He shivered in the cold, exhausted and dispirited. Others muttered in agreement.

C

"No," roared Bligh, at the top of his voice. "Have you forgotten your promise so soon? You'll have nought but your ration. If you think it's bad now, just wait for a while."

In his log he wrote: "I was sacredly determined with my life, to make what provisions I had to last eight weeks, let the daily proportion be ever so small." He had worked out that, all going well, they should reach Timor in eight weeks.

His fears about the weather proved correct. The first day was merely a sample of what was to come. For fifteen long, dreary days the bad weather continued. By day and night the men were soaking wet and freezing cold, with rain pouring down and the sea breaking over them. During all that time their food was only one twenty-fifth of a pound of bread (a small mouthful), and a quarter of a pint of water, for breakfast, dinner and supper. An occasional mouthful of pork and a teaspoon of rum were added.

At first Bligh measured out the rations by guesswork, but then he made scales from two coconut shells, with a pistol ball for weight, so that everyone received an exact amount. He arranged it so that half the men could partly lie down and the others sit up at a time, hoping in this way to let them have some sleep. He also made them regularly strip off their clothes and wring them out in salt water. This, he believed, gave them some warmth.

For all this, they were miserably, agonizingly, cold, wet, cramped and hungry. Everyone complained of severe pains, and many begged for more to eat. But Bligh was adamant. He sat hunched up at the end of the boat, over the chests of precious food, rarely sleeping himself, and doggedly making the men do what he knew was best for them. Without his iron will, many of them would have lain down and died during the first few days.

In addition, this amazing man wrote in his log every day, kept an exact account of what was eaten, what distance he reckoned they travelled, what the estimated latitude and longitude was, and desscribed the many islands they passed. Among these were what are now called the Fiji Islands, and Bligh was the first white man to discover and note them. With his passion for accuracy, it disturbed him greatly not to be able to map them properly.

"Being constantly wet," he wrote in the log, "it is with the utmost difficulty I can open a book to write and I am now only too sensible that I can do no more than point out where these lands may be found again. It is impossible for me to be very correct. The sketch I have made will give a comparative view of their extent. I believe all the large islands are inhabited, as they appeared very fertile."

Much as they needed food, the small ship's company did not dare land on these rich-looking islands, and at one stage terror again seized them. Several canoes put out from one of the islands and started to pursue the small launch. Fortunately, the natives gave up after a little while, probably afraid of getting too far away from their own land, and so the men in the launch breathed freely again.

As the days passed, the weather became steadily worse, and on May 18, twenty days after the mutiny, we find Bligh growing afraid for his small company.

"At dawn," he wrote in his log, "some of my people seemed half dead; our appearances were horrible; and I could look no way but I caught the eye of some one in distress. Extreme hunger was now too evident, but no one suffered from thirst. . . . I endeavoured to prove that we were more happy in our present situation than if we had fair weather."

Still the storm and rain continued, and on May 22, it appeared as if they could last no longer.

"Our situation this day," wrote Bligh, "was extremely calamitous. We were obliged to take the course of the sea, running right before it, and watching with the utmost care, as the least error in the helm would in a moment have been our destruction."

As night came, there was no relief in sight. "The misery we suffered this night," he continued, "exceeded the preceding. The sea flew over us with great force, and kept us baling with horror and anxiety. At dawn of day I found every one in a most distressed condition, and I began to fear that another such night would put an end to the lives of several, who seemed no longer able to support their sufferings. I served an allowance of two teaspoonfuls of rum, after drinking which, having wrung our clothes and taken our breakfast of bread and water, we became a little refreshed."

Then, just when hope seemed at its lowest ebb, just when the men felt they could endure no more, the weather changed. At last, on May 24, just twenty-six days after the mutiny, the sun came out again. The men were able to strip off their clothes and dry them, and the warmth of the sun took some of the pain from their aching bodies.

The seas grew calm, and Bligh, too, after the vigilance of days and nights of storms, wet and cold, was able to relax a little. One can imagine him looking around at his exhausted men, and wondering what strange fate had brought him to this situation. From the beginning of his Naval career he had been conscientious, hard-working, devoted to his duty. When put in command, his first thought had always been the care of his men, and he was far ahead of other captains of his day in matters of diet for his crew and care of their health. Yet, here he was. Half his crew had mutinied against him, and he was cast adrift in a small boat.

He thought back on how he had gained command of the *Bounty*, through sheer hard work and ability. Ever since he had entered the Navy as a midshipman, his career had been a battle, an overcoming of obstacles. All around him he saw men of less ability being given promotion, through influence and money, in a Navy full of graft and corruption, while he was left behind.

All he had to offer was his intense devotion to duty and a determination to succeed. It was this determination that carried him through. As he had no influence, he had quickly seen that to gain promotion he would have to do something that would mark him out from his fellow midshipmen. He had therefore concentrated on navigation, surveying and map-making. He made himself perfect in these arts, working long days and long nights. Then came his reward.

In 1776, at the age of 23, he was picked out by Captain Cook, because of his outstanding ability in these fields, and he was made Master of H.M.S. *Resolution*, the larger of the two ships that were to sail around the world under the greatest of all English navigators.

It was the third of Captain Cook's famous voyages, the one on which he met his death, and Bligh thought back to that tragic occurrence. And he thought of the many other things that had happened during that voyage, how he, as Master, had taken a leading part in the extensive mapping and surveying done. Also, he thought of the many things he had learnt from Captain Cook, about diet, the care of crews, cleanliness, and about nautical surveying and cartography. All these things he carried out when he had a command of his own.

Suddenly his thoughts were brought back to the present.

" A booby! " one of the men shouted loudly. "A booby, sir!   I've caught a booby! "

E VERYONE in the boat was talking and laughing. A large bird had landed on the boat, and William Cole had caught it.

"A booby! A booby!" cried Bligh exultantly. "Now that's a catch, man. Hand it here and we'll have it for dinner."

All that day, since the storm had abated, a few birds had been flying around the launch. There had also been branches floating in the water, and these signs, added to Bligh's reckoning, made him believe they must be getting near the coast of New Holland. That was good news enough, but now they had a bird for dinner as well, a bird about the size of a duck! No wonder everyone looked happier. Amid much laughter, the bird was given to Robert Lamb, the butcher, to kill, and then Bligh cut it into eighteen pieces, including even its entrails, beak and feet. He gave its blood to three of the men whose health worried him most.

"Whose getting the best of the other bits?" asked Purcell suspiciously.

"We'll decide by *Who Shall Have This?* That's the best idea," replied Bligh jovially. "Mr. Fryer! Turn your back, and call out the names when I point to each portion."

This was a way well known at sea for sharing among sailors. One person turns his back on what has been divided, and another points separately to each part, each time asking, "Who shall have this?" The person with his back turned calls out a different name each time, and that person has the part pointed to. After that, every day, one or more boobies were caught. They were called boobies, because the sailors had found them slow, stupid birds. One can imagine the relish with which the men ate these added tit-bits, and how their spirits must have lifted at even this small change in diet and the knowledge that they were nearing land.

With the continuing good weather and the raised spirits among the men, Bligh could once more spare time to think about the strange fate that had befallen him. He thought back to the return of Captain Cook's two ships in 1780, after four years at sea. He remembered his disappointment that, in spite of the part he had taken in the surveying and navigation during that long period, he was not made a Lieutenant.

He remembered too the holidays he spent on the Isle of Man, and the three families he came to know there, destined to play an important part in his life. One was the Bethams, and in 1781 he married Elizabeth Betham. The others were the Christians and the Heywoods, and both young Christian and young Heywood had been part of the crew of the *Bounty*, at the special request of their families. Yet both had mutinied against him. Christian had sailed under him twice before, and always he had gone out of his way to advise and encourage him.

At last Bligh's promotion to Lieutenant had come, late in 1781, and also the payment of £1,000 as his share in the royalties of the book he helped to write on Captain Cook's Third Voyage.

Then, after serving in several other ships, had come what he had longed for—his first single command in the Navy. He was put in charge of the *Bounty*, to ship breadfruit trees from the South Seas, where they grew in such great numbers, to the West Indies, where the British planters needed food for their slaves. Bligh remembered his excitement when Sir Joseph Banks, the famous naturalist, who had been with Captain Cook when he discovered Australia, explained the plan to him.

But disappointment had followed the good news about the *Bounty*. Bligh remembered how both he and Sir Joseph had been amazed at the scanty way in which the expedition was equipped. There was only one small ship of 215 tons, and a crew of only 45 men. There were no commissioned officers other than Bligh, and he, though Captain of the ship, still remained a Lieutenant. Worst of all, no marines were to sail with them. Cook's expeditions had always carried marines, to keep the sailors in order. No wonder the mutineers on the *Bounty* had found their task so easy! And this thought brought Bligh back to the mutiny again.

Christian! he thought bitterly. That Christian whose family he had known since he was a junior Lieutenant, should do this! Yes, thought Bligh, it all came back to Christian. In his determination to return to Otaheite he had talked the men into mutiny. It would not be too difficult, either. He remembered there had been an attempted mutiny on Captain Cook's last voyage, but the marines had quickly put it down. He remembered other times when members of the crews had tried to escape, but had been captured. The soft living of the

South Seas had always made the rough sailors want to stay there.

Bligh thought of how, in spite of his disappointment at the size of the breadfruit expedition, he had determined it would be a success. He had spared nothing, absolutely nothing, to make it so, to ensure the safety and health of his men, and to transplant and care for the breadfruit trees in the best possible manner. He had taken a fiddler so that his men would have music to dance to, he had carefully watched their diet.

When cold wet weather hit them, he had kept fires burning below and had made the men change their clothes. Sometimes they had not liked it, but he had insisted. He had punished them less than any Captain he knew. There were far less floggings on his ships than on those of Captain Cook. He could not forgive the men for forgetting all these things and taking the boat.

But, he thought, his mouth setting into a grim, straight line, he would not be defeated. He had brought this suffering band of men this far, and he was determined to get them safely back to England. The next danger would be landing on the coast of New Holland. He knew only too well how tricky were those long, dangerous coral reefs stretching down the coast, for he had been through them with Cook. Yet get through them they must, for they needed the rest, shelter and food that the calm waters on the other side would give them.

So, for the next two days, he kept unceasing vigilance, and then, on May 28, he saw the white foam of ocean breakers, hurling themselves on the reefs, and, beyond them, smooth water.

Keeping well out to sea, they sailed north, Bligh scanning the coast for a break. After a few anxious hours, he suddenly saw one, and then, with the greatest of skill, he manoeuvred the ship into the calm waters beyond the waves breaking on the cruel teeth of the jagged coral. They soon found an island, and for the first time in 26 days the men were able to step off their cramped, uncomfortable boat on to dry, warm land.

"We now returned God thanks," wrote Bligh in his log, "for His gracious protection, and with much content took our miserable allowance of a twenty-fifth of a pound of bread and a quarter of a pint of water for dinner."

For the next week the small launch made its way slowly up the placid waters inside the Great Barrier Reef, stopping each night on an island. For the first time in weeks the men were able to lie down to sleep. Stews were made each night from a mixture of oysters and clams found on the islands, with sometimes a little pork added, and parts of plants and palms as vegetables. These were cooked on fires lit with a piece of brimstone and a tinder-box. Berries that could be eaten were also found, and a small supply of birds was caught.

But peace did not last for long.

People united in the face of great danger often fall out once the danger is past. This happened here. Quarrels broke out among the men. The Master, Mr. Fryer, and Purcell, the carpenter, complained they were not getting enough of the food. At another time, Fryer insisted on having a fire of his own, which blazed so brightly that Bligh was afraid it would bring natives from the mainland. Someone stole some of the last pieces of precious pork, and others gorged themselves on too many berries, and were sick.

All this made Bligh very angry, and when Purcell, always a trouble-maker, refused to obey an order of Bligh's he felt that action was necessary.

"I'm as good a man as you, Mr. Bligh," Purcell shouted.

Bligh's ever ready anger blazed forth, both at the man's insolence, and also because he knew that if the men did not obey him completely, they would never reach home.

"You think so, do you?" he shouted back. Then he grabbed hold of a cutlass and brandished it at Purcell. "All right, my good man," he said scornfully, pointing to where another cutlass lay, "then take hold of a cutlass for yourself, and prove it to me. We'll see who's the better man."

Purcell did not take up the challenge. He slunk away in sulky silence, and Bligh was left master of his men. In all his career, Bligh never lacked the courage, either physical or moral, to stand by his opinions, and he had realized that here a show of physical force was the only way to subdue the discontented men. He knew he must make the men give him the absolute obedience that was still going to be necessary. The men seemed to think the journey practically over, but Bligh knew there were many miles to go and many obstacles to be faced.

Also the men were far from well. They were extremely weak, and all suffered from dizziness in the head, weakness and pain in the joints, and violent pains in their stomachs. The peaceful days inside the Barrier Reef were resting them, warming them, and allowing them to sleep properly, and without this break they would surely all have died. They were not, however, finding enough food to build them up, and Bligh realized that the sooner they continued their voyage the better.

So, after six days, when the northern part of New Holland was reached, the little vessel was once more launched into the open ocean. Bligh was amazed to find the men very cheerful. They had forgotten what the open ocean could do to them in a small, open launch, and they all spoke as if their journey was nearly over.

"Miserable as our situation was in every respect," he wrote in his log, "I was secretly surprised to see that it did not appear to affect any one so strongly as myself. On the contrary, it seemed as if they had embarked on a voyage to Timor in a vessel sufficiently calculated for safety and convenience. I encouraged everyone with the hope that eight or ten days would bring us to a land of safety; and after praying to God for a continuance of his most gracious protection, I served an allowance of water for supper."

A sign of the men's optimism was a demand by some for more of the food that was left, but Bligh's iron will continued to ration out their meagre supplies, and due to his control it was found that at this stage they still had enough bread for seventeen more days. The ration was thus slightly increased. They were also a few oysters and clams to add to the diet, but, try as he could, Bligh had been unable to build up a stock of birds during the journey up the coast of New Holland.

Bligh's fears about this part of the voyage were soon realized. Heavy seas hit them again, and the exhausted men, wet, cold and already weakened by their earlier ordeal, had to start bailing once more, night and day. This time the men had nothing with which to fight. No reserves of strength were left to them. The only ray of light was that practically each day a booby, sometimes two, were caught.

But for all that, the situation gradually became hopeless. The surgeon, Thomas Ledward, and the old sailmaker, Lawrence Lebogue, were so weak that daily they were thought to be dead. Bligh did what he could for them. He gave them the blood of the birds caught, and a teaspoon of wine each day, but each day he thought would be their last.

The rest of the crew were little better. Every man was growing so weak that any movement was difficult. Their legs became swollen, and their faces became mere skeletons with the skin, burned black by the sun, stretched over the bones. Many became partly unconscious and lost their understanding of what was happening.

Bligh was in much the same condition. One very touching part in his log reads: "The boatswain innocently told me that he really thought I looked worse than any one in the boat. The simplicity with which he uttered such an opinion amused me, and I returned him a better compliment." We can see here the real affection that existed between Bligh and the better members of the crew.

No matter what they wanted, Bligh had no intention of letting his men lie down and die. For all his own weakness, he still kept his iron control over them. In such physical distress, he still issued, three times a day, the exact small ration. He still kept some of the men bailing, and he still kept the watches going.

Then, just when once more it appeared as if they could endure no more, relief came.

"Land!" croaked William Cole, the boatswain. "Land!"

It was three in the morning of Friday, June 12, and the sight of land surely never brought greater joy to any collection of men than did the wooded slopes of Timor, rising up in the early morning light.

"It is not possible," wrote Bligh in his log, "for me to describe the pleasure which the blessing of the sight of this land diffused among us. It appeared scarce credible to ourselves, that in an open boat, and so poorly provided, we should have been able to reach the coast of Timor in forty-one days after leaving Tofoa, having in that time run by our log, a distance of 3,618 miles."

Fryer and Purcell made one last effort to make his task more difficult. They wanted to land immediately and search for food. The threat of natives and the fact that Bligh knew there was a Dutch settlement somewhere along the coast could not stop their complaining and demanding.

Once again Bligh felt as if his anger would consume him. He ordered the boat to go into the shore.

"All right," he then challenged the two men,

his voice hoarse, and his thin body shaking. "You want to get out! Then get out! We never want to see you again. D'you hear? Get out! "

But, of course, the two men again did not accept the challenge, and the small boat went on its weary way, and just before daylight, two days later, it sailed into the harbour of the small Dutch town of Koepang.

When the boat stopped, the men could scarcely move. They could not believe that their nightmare was over. Then some of the local people came running down to meet them, and sick, sore, helpless, like so many blackened scarecrows, they were lifted out of the boat, and carried or helped up the shore to the waiting, welcoming township.

B ACK in England, William Bligh's family were waiting for his return, wondering why he was longer than they had expected. In the many books where Bligh is shown as a tyrant and a bully, no hint is given of the love and gentleness he always showed towards his wife and daughters. Yet it is easy to find proof of it. His letters, many of which can still be read in their original form today, are full of it.

While his family were waiting and wondering, the men, far away in Koepang, were slowly regaining their health. The Dutch people of the small township took to their hearts immediately the pathetic group of emaciated men that staggered up the beach. They gave them food, clothing, shelter and medical attention, and the moment Bligh knew they were cared for, and felt some strength returning to his own body, he sat down to write to his beloved wife:

"Coepang in Timor,
19th August, 1789.
"My Dear Dear Betsy,
  I am now in a part of the world that I never expected; it is, however, a place that has afforded me relief and saved my life, and I have the happiness to assure you I am now in perfect health.

  What an emotion does my heart and soul feel that I have once more an opportunity of writing to you and my little angels, and particularly as you have all been so near losing the best of friends, when you would have had no person to have regarded you as I do, and you must have spent the remainder of your days without knowledge of what was become of me, or what would have been still worse, to have known I had been starved to death at sea or destroyed by Indians—all these dreadful circumstances I have combated with success, and in the most extraordinary manner that ever happened, never despairing from the first moment of my disaster that I should overcome all my difficulties.

Know then, my own dear Betsy, I have lost the Bounty . . ."

Bligh went on in the letter to tell Betsy briefly about the mutiny and the voyage in the small boat. He completed the letter as follows:

"Give my blessing to my dear Harriet, my dear Mary, and my dear Betsy, and to my dear little stranger, and tell them I shall soon be home. To you, my love, I give all that an affectionate husband can give—love, respect, all that is or ever will be in the power of your ever affectionate friend and husband.

Wm. Bligh."

"The dear little stranger" in the letter was the expected fourth baby that had not been born when Bligh sailed on the Bounty. Little did he know that it was twin girls. He was really therefore writing to five "little angels", not four.

He also sent much longer reports of the tragedy to the Admiralty, to Sir Joseph Banks, and to Duncan Campbell, a ship-owning uncle of his wife's, who had helped him with his career. It is heart-breaking to read these long letters—some take twelve pages of print—and to realize that they all had to be written by hand by a very sick man.

During those days in Koepang, Bligh suffered almost constantly from excruciating headaches and fevers. The headaches were to haunt and harass him for the rest of his life. Neither he, nor the rest of his companions, ever completely recovered from the long open boat voyage.

What *did* happen to the other men?

While they were in the launch under his eye, Bligh had watched them like a hawk. But when he had brought them safely back to land, he could no longer watch or control their every movement, and six of them did not reach England alive.

In some cases it was no fault of the men. David Nelson, the botanist, had been one of the best of them, but he died of fever soon after Bligh's party of men reached land. Ledward, the surgeon, another good man, was washed overboard on the voyage by ship back to England. But the other four men probably ate and drank too much too quickly when they reached land, before their bodies could stand it.

Of the nineteen men the mutineers cast adrift, only twelve finally reached home.

Bligh himself arrived in England on March 14, 1790, and immediately found himself famous. He was the hero of the day. Everyone was talking about his courage, skill and daring in undertaking the longest small boat journey in history. There were articles written about him in magazines and newspapers, and a play was put on at the Royalty

Theatre called *The Pirates* or *The Calamities of Captain Bligh*. He was asked to give lectures, and was presented to the King, George III.

All his spare time was spent on writing a book, about the mutiny and the voyage, which was published before the end of 1790, and became a great success. The people in Jamaica, although he failed to take them the breadfruit trees, were so grateful for his attempt, that they granted him a gift of five hundred guineas, a great deal of money for those days.

As to his standing at the Admiralty, and with his friends, there was no shadow of criticism about his actions, and Sir Joseph Banks had nothing but sympathy for what had happened. As a matter of form, the Navy held a court-martial on the loss of the *Bounty*, and honourably acquitted Lieutenant Bligh and those with him of being responsible for her loss.

The Admiralty went further than merely acquitting him. They showed their confidence in him by promoting him first to Commander and then a month later to Post-Captain, without his having to serve the usual three years as Commander. Then, early in 1791, came, as far as Bligh was concerned, the best news of all. He was to be given another command to transplant breadfruit trees from Otaheite to the West Indies.

His wife and his little daughters all went down to Portsmouth with him to see over the ships that were being fitted out for the expedition. They went by coach, Betsy and the two eldest girls, Harriet and Mary, both dressed in red bonnets and long red cloaks.

They gazed with pride at the two ships that were to be under their father's command.

"Are both those ships to be yours, Papa?" asked Harriet.

"Yes, indeed. The *Providence* and the *Assistant*."

"The *Assistant* is very small, Papa," gasped Mary. "Can she sail right round the world?"

Bligh laughed at her. "I'll see that she does," he replied confidently. "She's only a small brig, you know, to help us with navigating and mapping. We're to make a complete chart of the Torres Strait, as well as transplant the breadfruit. But I'll see she returns safely."

Bligh's wife sighed. "They are doing you very well this time, William dear," she said. "Two ships, marines to keep order, more men! If only they had treated you the same last time."

Bligh's brows suddenly drew together in such anger that Betsy wished she had not mentioned the matter.

"You're are right, my dear. They stinted us of everything last time. But even so," he continued, speaking even more angrily, "we'd have done it. We'd have done it! Everything was going perfectly until that scoundrel Fletcher Christian . . ."

"Can we go on the ships, please, Papa?" asked Harriet.

"Yes, my dears, of course. We'll go on the *Providence*, and I'll show you the cabins specially fitted out ready to take the pots with the breadfruit in them."

As they climbed up the ladder on the side of the ship, a young midshipman stepped forward to

help first the little girls, then Mrs. Bligh.
"Betsy," said Bligh, as he too came aboard, "this
is Mr. Flinders, one of the young midshipmen
who is sailing with me. He has been recommended
by Captain Pasley, as a young man with special
interest in mapping and charting. Isn't that so,
Mr. Flinders?"

"Yes, sir."

"Well, I'm glad to see you down here showing
an interest in the boat," continued Bligh, as they
walked away.

The young midshipman was Matthew Flinders,
another name destined to become great in sea exploration. Flinders was the first man to sail and
chart completely around Australia. On this, his
first long sea voyage, the naval science, the knowledge of cartography and surveying that he would
learn from being for two years under the exacting
and expert captaincy of Bligh, would contribute
much towards his future career.

Thus we see the line of experience and knowledge in surveying, sea exploration and cartography passed down through three great men, Captain Cook to Captain Bligh, and Captain Bligh to
Captain Flinders. What Bligh learned from Cook,
he was able to hand on to Flinders.

The two ships finally sailed on August 3, 1791,
and on this voyage everything went according to
plan. Important discoveries and charts were made
in Tasmania, on the way to Otaheite, and in the
Fiji Islands and the Torres Strait, on the way home.
In Torres Strait, an attack by natives was success-
fully defeated. Then, in the middle of 1793,
breadfruit plants were delivered to the island of

St. Helena, at St. Vincent, and at Jamaica. Again, the Jamaican Government showed their appreciation by making a gift of 1,000 guineas to Bligh.

The two small ships reached home in September, after an absence of just over two years, successful in everything they had set out to achieve.

How strange then that the homecoming was not a happy one, for Bligh now found himself out of favour with the Admiralty. While he was away, events had been taking place in England that were to turn many people in high places against him. They were events over which he had no control. They were completely unjust. He was thousands of miles away, and quite unable to say anything in his own defence, and yet these events were to give him an undeserved reputation that has lasted right down to the present day.

They concerned the fate of the twenty-five mutineers of the *Bounty* who turned Bligh and the eighteen other men adrift.

WHEN Bligh was finally cast adrift, there was great confusion on the *Bounty*. Some of the mutineers were jubilant, but some were divided in their thoughts, and a few were appalled at what had happened.

Fletcher Christian quickly took control, but if he thought he could keep it, he was mistaken. The men who did not want to work for Bligh were no more willing to work for Christian. For a while, however, things went smoothly, and by June the *Bounty* was back at Otaheite. Christian had no intention of staying there. So, with fresh supplies and some of the native men and women, the *Bounty* left almost immediately for another island near by.

Here the men started to build a fort, but quarrels soon broke out, for the men objected to the hard work that Christian imposed on them. Quarrels also broke out between the white men and the natives that lived on the island and resented the white men. Many natives were killed, and the mutineers began to feel that their own lives were in danger.

"Let's go back to Otaheite," said Morrison.

"That's what I say," agreed Musprat. "Livin' is easy there. There's more food, an' the natives 'ere'll kill us in our sleep one night."

"Don't be stupid," growled McKoy. "D'yer
56

want to 'ave the 'ole British Navy on yer tracks?"

"We don't mind," replied Coleman. "We had no part in the mutiny."

The arguments continued. Some feared to go back to Otaheite. Others wanted to, either because they were innocent, or because they were foolish enough to think they would be left there in peace by the authorities at home. Finally a vote was taken. Sixteen decided to return to Otaheite, and nine to go elsewhere. So the *Bounty* returned to Otaheite, and the arms and ammunition were divided between them. Then the small ship, with nine white men and their native wives and some native men, sailed away again, leaving the rest behind.

The *Bounty* was never to be seen again by the outside world, and the mutineers on her were never to face the punishment they deserved.

After some wandering they finally settled on Pitcairn Island, a perfect hiding place. It had a hidden harbour and a fruitful countryside. Land was given to each man and the *Bounty* burnt, in order to destroy any evidence against them. But the mutineers were not happy. They fought among themselves and they fought with the native men. In a few years Fletcher Christian and five of the others became so hated by the native men, for their ill treatment and cruelty, that the natives killed them. William McKoy threw himself over a cliff in a fit of drunkenness.

This left Edward Young and Alexander Smith, or John Adams, as he now called himself. Their story is a strange one. Gradually they began to lead reformed lives. They began church services, grace before meals, and school for the nineteen children that were born to the mutineers. Young died in 1800, but Adams carried on the work, and lived until 1829.

It was not until 1808 that the island was discovered, by an American trading ship. When the Captain went ashore he found there only John Adams, an old man, several natives and several good-looking children, the offspring of the mutineers and their native wives. Other American ships visited the island from time to time, but the English authorities did not bother about it. John Adams died in peace, and direct descendants of these people still live on Pitcairn Island today.

Meanwhile, back to Otaheite, the mutineers who stayed there suffered even more than those that went away. In a story that is tragedy and violence from beginning to end what happened to these men is probably the most tragic part of all. It must be remembered that at least four of these men, Coleman, the armourer, Norman and McIntosh, the carpenters' mates, and Byrne, the blind fiddler, were definitely innocent. They had all begged to be allowed to go with Bligh in the launch, and when Bligh sailed on the second breadfruit journey, he left a written record of the innocence of these men. Others, if not completely innocent, were certainly not as guilty as the ringleaders. Yet all shared the same fate.

While Bligh, back in London, was getting ready for the second breadfruit journey, a Captain Edwards of H.M.S. *Pandora* was ordered to sail to the South Seas to try and capture the *Bounty* mutineers. It so happened that Edwards was one of the most brutal and foul-mouthed captains of his day.

The *Pandora* reached Otaheite in March, 1791. Immediately some of the mutineers gave themselves up, while others had to be captured. Two had already been killed. When they were all collected on board ship, Captain Edwards acted towards them with the greatest inhumanity imaginable. He had a wooden coop, eighteen feet by eleven, built on deck. It was named " Pandora's Box ", and in this box the men stayed, manacled hand and feet, day and night, through cold, wet and intense heat. Their sufferings were unbelievable.

The *Pandora* spent some time looking for the other mutineers, but, unsuccessful, she then sailed for home, and was wrecked on the Great Barrier Reef of Australia. While the ship was sinking, Edwards refused to allow the men out of their coop, and even ordered extra sentinels. Fortunately, some of the crew disobeyed his orders, and opened the hatch at the last moment. But four of the men were drowned.

For the rest of the voyage, Edwards continued his inhumane treatment, having the men manacled in various jails and on board ship until they reached home, there to face their trial.

This was in June 1792, about a year after Bligh had set sail on the second breadfruit journey. Friends and relatives of the mutineers immediately set about preparing for the trial, to take place in September, three months later, and a year before Bligh returned to England again. It was most unfair that the trial took place in his absence, for he was unable to give evidence or to deny things that were said of him.

There was obviously only one way to clear the names of the mutineers, and that was to try and show they had a good reason for mutiny. Thus we had friends and relatives of the guilty men writing letters to the papers, articles, and even books, to show that Bligh was a tyrant and a bully, a cruel commander, a foul-mouthed man, a man who starved and beat his crew. The most intemperate language was used against him.

The main storm centred around young Peter Heywood, one of the youngest of the mutineers, a midshipman of only seventeen, and a young man whom Bligh took with him as a special favour to the Heywood family. Peter Heywood had powerful friends in the Admiralty and a devoted family. Everything was done to prove his innocence, and, when the court martial did condemn him to death, to get him a pardon.

When he returned home Bligh heard the full story from Betsy.

"They acquitted the four men you said were innocent, William," she explained, "but it is terrible to think what they suffered on the journey home."

"Yes! Yes! So I believe," he replied impatiently. "And so they should. Didn't I leave instructions about their innocence? But what's this I hear of Heywood," he continued angrily. "What's this I hear?"

"Yes, dear. It's true. They pardoned him, at the last moment. Morrison and Musprat too. But they hanged Ellison, Burkitt and Millward."

"Pardoned Heywood! Pardoned Heywood! I can't believe it. He was a mutineer if ever there was one. Grinning and taking their side!"

"But he was so young, dear."

"He knew what he was up to. I'll never forgive him."

"Don't worry about it, dear. After all your second voyage was a tremendous success, and now you're safely home with us again."

Bligh's anger faded immediately. He smiled at his wife. "To be home with you and all my little daughters is more important than anything else. If only I could remain here forever."

But a few days later he was fuming again. He had just returned from the Admiralty.

"D'you know what, dear? They kept me waiting in the outer rooms for hours. And then they didn't receive me. Someone's blackening my name, Betsy, so that young Peter Heywood can get promotion. As long as there's a stain on his name, he won't get it. So they're going to put a stain on *my* name now. I won't have it, d'you hear? I won't have it."

Again Betsy was able to soothe him down, but a year later worse was to follow. The Christians now joined the Heywoods in defiling Bligh. Fletcher Christian's brother, a clever barrister, brought out a long and untrue description of the *Bounty* voyage. To save the name of the family, he gave what appeared fair and logical reasons for the mutiny, making Bligh appear a tyrant and Fletcher the innocent victim.

There was never any doubt of Fletcher Christian's guilt. Everyone who survived the mutiny was of one accord that he was the ring-leader, and that the main reason for the mutiny was his wish to return to Otaheite. For many years, however, a very different picture was presented.

Whether Peter Heywood was innocent or not will never be known. He was certainly not a ring-leader, but he did nothing to prevent the mutiny. Nor did he lean over the side and call out his innocence to Bligh, as did four of the men, thus risking the anger of the mutineers. Reading through the evidence carefully, one cannot help feeling that Peter Heywood did have some sympathy towards the mutineers and certainly none towards his Captain. Bligh was strongly of the opinion that he was guilty.

Whatever the truth is, it was most unfortunate that books written by his supporters, and by Fletcher Christian's relatives, should have been taken as a basis for so many future histories and books of fiction on the events. The famous Holly-wood film, *Mutiny on the Bounty*, even twisted the story to put Bligh in the place of Captain Edwards, so that Bligh is shown as going back to capture the mutineers, and as being responsible for "Pandora's Box" and all the other inhumani-ties of Captain Edwards.

IF the Admiralty did treat Bligh coolly on his return from the second breadfruit voyage, and if influence did gain Peter Heywood a pardon and promotion, it was soon forgotten. Bligh was far too capable a man to be long out of favour. Within eighteen months he was given charge of the *Calcutta*, and, less than a year later, he was transferred to the *Director*, a battleship with 64 guns, which formed part of Admiral Duncan's fleet against the Dutch.

While in command of the *Director*, Bligh took part in the battle of Camperdown in 1797, where the British fleet under Admiral Duncan soundly defeated the Dutch. During the battle, Bligh himself was partly responsible for capturing the Dutch flag ship, the *Vryheid*.

His next command was the H.M.S. *Glatton*, and while on this ship he fought under Nelson in the Battle of Copenhagen, 1801, when practically the whole of the Danish fleet was either sunk or captured. It was a long, exacting battle, and Bligh's ship was in the forefront of the fighting all day and suffered great losses. At the end, Nelson called Bligh on board his ship, and praised his action.

During the next four years he was transferred to the command of even larger ships, carrying 74 guns, and, whenever there was a lull in naval work or fighting, he was used by the Navy to survey and chart several of the ports and harbours on the English and Irish coasts.

Another interesting event took place during these years. It is worth special mention, because it is another one of the many things that those who seek to hate Bligh have described quite unfairly.

Back in 1797, when Bligh was in command of the *Director*, the Mutiny at the Nore broke out. This was part of a general mutiny among sailors throughout the whole fleet. The conditions under which sailors and soldiers worked in those days were appalling. Their food, their living quarters, their pay were hardly worthy of animals. In addition, as soon as danger to the country was passed, the navy or army would be reduced, and many of the men dismissed. Also some of the commanders had shocking records for cruelty.

The result of this was mutiny, and all commanders were ordered by the sailors to leave the ships. William Bligh was one of these. The mutiny did not concern him personally, yet his detractors quote this as another example of how his crew mutinied against him because of his brutality.

The truth is very different. Bligh was actually one of the last commanders to have to leave his ship, and was used by the Admiralty to negotiate with the mutineers. Moreover, when the mutiny was over, the mutineers were asked to draw up a list of the commanders against whom they had grievances. William Bligh was not on that list. Again, when the mutiny was over, and those in command were intending to punish thirty-one men from his ship, we find Bligh working hard to have most of them pardoned. In the end all but ten escaped punishment.

Bligh always took a personal, almost fatherly interest in his men. It was because of this, and because he was prepared to give extra time to instruct or help them, that he became irritable and short-tempered when they were careless or stupid. It also made him bitterly angry against such people as Peter Heywood or Fletcher Christian, whom he felt had been ungrateful.

Although not a breath of cruelty can be proved against him, there is no doubt that his career was studded with outbursts of temper when he found his men lazy or incompetent. The moment the outburst was over, Bligh forgot about it. Most of the people under him looked on him with affection and took his outbursts as they were meant. Every now and then, however, there would be one who seemed unable to forgive being belittled in front of others, or unable to forget Bligh's tactless words. These people became his enemies, and were only too willing to spread rumours about him. These outbursts of temper, this irritability, this intolerance with inefficient people, seemed to increase as Bligh grew older, possibly because of the headaches that he suffered as an aftermath of the long open-boat voyage.

None of these things, however, made those in authority think less of him. He was known as a thoroughly capable, brave commander. He was also known to be of very strong character, and to be one who would not give up no matter what were the odds against him. No one who knew of the struggle he had to get on in the navy, or of his

E

doggedness in the long voyage in the open boat, could doubt these things. And it was because of these things that his career now took a most surprising turn.

For the first time the name of New South Wales came to mean something of importance to the Bligh family.

One of the men who seemed really to understand Bligh, and who never lost faith in him through all the ups and downs of his career, was Sir Joseph Banks. Sir Joseph Banks had become something of an authority on the small struggling colony of New South Wales, clinging grimly to one small part of the large continent of New Holland, or Australia.

This colony was now badly in need of a new, very strong Governor. The last two Governors, Hunter and King, had met with every sort of difficulty and opposition. The Army officers stationed in New South Wales refused to carry out instructions for the good of the colony. Instead, they ran the colony for their own good. Hunter and King had been powerless against them, and it was obvious that a man of iron was needed to make the Army and the wealthy settlers obey the laws.

Sir Joseph Banks was consulted by the Colonial Office, and he immediately thought of Bligh. As a result we find him writing to Bligh early in 1805:

In conversation, I was this day asked if I knew a man proper to be sent out in Governor King's stead—one who has integrity unimpeached, a mind capable of providing its own resources in difficulties, without leaning on others for advice, firm in discipline, civil in deportment and not subject to whimper and whine when severity of discipline is wanted. I immediately answered; as this man must be chosen from among the post captains, I knew of no one but Captain Bligh who will suit. . . .

Banks went on to say that whereas the previous governors had been receiving an income of £1,000 per year, Bligh would be paid £2,000. This was surely an indication of the value those in authority put on him.

The offer, of course, turned the Bligh household upside down.

"What d'you think of it, Betsy? What do you think?" asked William excitedly.

"I cannot bear to think of it," replied Betsy. She was completely dismayed. She and William were now grandparents, for Harriet, their eldest daughter, was married with two small sons. Mary, their second daughter, was also married, to John Putland, a Naval Lieutenant.

"I could never stand that long sea voyage, William," she said in despair. "You know I get sick if I am on a ship for two hours. And to leave my children and my grandchildren! I am too old, William, to start sailing around the world. And we could not take all the girls with us, right to the other side of the world. It would be wrong, I feel sure."

Much discussion followed. Bligh was disappointed, yet he felt that Betsy was right. Sir Joseph Banks was consulted again and again. He pointed out how good the opportunity was. Bligh was no longer young, and this would carry a pension of £1,000 a year when the job was over. Moreover, his rank in the Navy would continue. He even pointed out that it could mean a black mark against Bligh if he refused the appointment.

Suddenly, a way was seen around their troubles. Mary's husband, Lieutenant John Putland, would go out with Bligh as his aide-de-camp, and Mary would go with them, to act as the Governor's lady. Mrs. Bligh would stay at home to care for the rest of the family. Betsy was not happy about it, but she felt it was the best that could be done. She faced years of separation, but was, after all, used to it.

So, in February 1806, Mrs. Bligh once more bade farewell to her husband. This time her second daughter and her son-in-law went also. They sailed in a convoy of ships, taking many more convicts, packed below decks, and some free settlers, as well as the new Governor, to the far away colony of New South Wales.

AROUND about 1780, the gaols of England were full of prisoners, living in unbelievable squalor, some guilty of the blackest of crimes, others of practically nothing, and all condemned to be transported out of England. But there was nowhere for them to go since the American colonies had freed themselves from British rule.

Then someone suggested New Holland. So, in 1788, Governor Arthur Phillip was sent out from England with eleven ships, carrying 717 convicts and 290 other people, Army officers, marines, wives and children, to make a settlement in the unexplored, unknown continent.

It was a badly planned and badly equipped expedition, sent away hurriedly, to get rid of people who were becoming a problem. They were unfit to start a new country and they found themselves in a hostile land. From this strange beginning grew the great Commonwealth of Australia.

The country was not hostile in the way one may imagine. There were no dangerous animals, no poisonous plants, no fierce natives. It was hostile in its complete indifference to the early settlers. It offered no fruits or native plants that could be cultivated to provide food, and no animals that could be domesticated. The harbour that was chosen for the first settlement was superbly beautiful to look at, but with a surrounding countryside that proved to be hemmed in by mountains, and niggardly in yielding good crops. The men that Governor Phillip had to work with knew little or nothing about building houses or planting wheat.

In this struggling, wretched collection of human beings and poor dwellings, Governor Phillip gradually brought order out of the chaos. Better land was found on the Parramatta and Hawkesbury rivers. The best of the convicts were given grants and they started farms for themselves. When, after four years, ill-health forced Governor Phillip to return home, he left the colony almost able to keep itself in the necessities of life.

But Australia was not to grow in any normal fashion. Before Phillip left Australia, the marines he brought with him to police the settlement had been replaced by the New South Wales Corps. This corps was specially recruited for the work, and was of the poorest type of soldier. Commissions were sold and men were enlisted wherever they could be found. The best of England's soldiers were busy fighting Napoleon, and only those with little future at home were interested in going thousands of miles away to a new colony.

It was a tragedy that Phillip left before a new Governor arrived. It was not until three years later, in 1805, that the new Governor, Governor Hunter, arrived to take over. In those three years, the military ran the country to suit themselves and their friends. Large grants of land were made to officers. They were given the pick of the convict labour, while public works were neglected. They were given complete control of the sale of goods, and could charge what prices they liked. Worst of all, they were allowed to import as much rum and strong drink into the country as they chose, and to keep control over the selling of it.

When a ship came into port, with goods for the colony, or with rum, the officers and their friends would buy up all the cargo. They would then resell these goods at huge profits. They would often insist on a farmer taking rum for his wheat instead of money; or perhaps they would give him goods that the farmer did not want. Imagine getting a few gallons of rum for a year's hard work in the fields! Some of the officers even insisted on the soldiers taking their pay in rum or other goods estimated for the purpose at many times their true value.

Because of all this, the officers and their friends became wealthy. They acquired large amounts of land. When a small settler was ruined, they would buy his land for more rum. Public works were neglected while the convicts worked on the land belonging to the military. In the face of it all, the poor people were completely helpless. The New South Wales Corps were the only strength in the colony. They were meant to keep order, but they were the men that were doing so much harm. Even the civil courts were put under the control of the military leaders.

This was the position that Governor Hunter found when he landed in Australia in 1795. He issued orders that these practices were to stop, but the men who should have carried out his orders flouted them. They refused to do as they were told.

One of the leaders of the rum traders was John Macarthur, an ambitious, unscrupulous man, who had come out as an officer in the New South Wales Corps. Later on, when he found out how easy it was to make money by farming and trade, he resigned from the Corps. John Macarthur used all the means mentioned above to acquire great wealth and much land, where he carried out experiments in sheep-breeding.

John Macarthur was a born trouble-maker. He was always quarrelling with someone. He would pick a fight when it suited him, and then, again when it suited him, he would make use of his magnetic personality to become a close friend of the person with whom he had fought. He could twist things so that he always appeared in the right, and other people in the wrong.

In one of despatches home, Hunter wrote about him :

> There is not a person in this colony whose opinions I hold in greater contempt than I do this busybody's, because I have ever observed that under the most specious and plausible of them there has always been cover'd a self-interested motive.

Macarthur and his friends did everything they could to make the new Governor's life a misery. They insulted him. They brought law actions against his supporters, and, because the military controlled the courts, these actions would be upheld. They sent letters to the Government at home, criticizing and falsifying everything he did. After five years, Hunter could carry on no longer and was replaced by Governor King.

King was no more successful. He started with

great optimism, but when the same tactics were used against him, he soon found his task was hopeless. The very men who should have been his strength were the men he had to fight. So the public works remained unfinished, the wealthy grew wealthier and the big monopolies remained. King, too, found that John Macarthur was the archenemy, the ring leader.

His behaviour was so bad, that King sent him home to be tried. With the evidence of his misdeeds, King wrote as follows:

"I need not inform you who or what Captain Macarthur is. He came here in 1790 more than £500 in debt, and is now worth at least £20,000. . . . His employment during the eleven years he has been here has been that of making a large fortune, helping his brother officers to make small ones (mostly at the publick expence), and sowing discord and strife. . . . Experience has convinced every man in this colony that there are no resources which art, cunning, impudence and a pair of baselick eyes can afford that he does not put in practice to obtain any point he undertakes. . . ."

Such was Macarthur's cunning, that the evidence against him disappeared from the despatch box on the way to England, and Macarthur returned, not in disgrace, but with authority for a further grant of 5,000 acres on which to conduct his sheep-breeding experiments. He had worked his way into a close friendship with officials in the Colonial Office. His sheep-breeding experiments did in fact prove very important, but there were others who were also carrying them out in

Australia, without acquiring tremendous wealth, overturning governors, and depriving the needy.

This was the end of King. He felt he could struggle no more. Then the news suddenly reached Sydney that the Government at home was replacing Governor King by Governor Bligh, giving him strict instructions to stop trade in spirits in the colony.

The drawing-rooms of the colony and the Officer's Mess were immediately full of gossip and stories. All the worst that had ever been said of Bligh was told, re-told and exaggerated. All the old accusations about the mutiny on the *Bounty* were brought out. The trouble-makers made sure that before Bligh even reached the colony he was known as a tyrant and a bully, who was to succeed where Hunter and King had failed.

What did the Government at home expect to happen? On one hand was Macarthur, a clever, scheming, hot-tempered man, who, with his allies, had not the slightest intention of losing their privileges and positions. On the other hand stood Bligh, a man of iron will, who would never let himself be thrust aside as had Hunter and King. An order to him was an order. If the Government at home told him to stop the trading in rum in the Colony and to help the small farmers, then this he would do, even if it meant standing alone against the whole New South Wales Corps.

Governor William Bligh, his daughter Mary, and her husband, Lieutenant Putland, first saw this colony, where so much strife had already taken place, and where so much more was yet to come, in August 1806. The first sight of Sydney Harbour, with its blue seas and countless, tree-covered head-lands stretching into the water, left them breath-less. The sight of Sydney Town was just as sur-prising, but in a different way.

"Is that all it is, Papa?" asked Mary, staring in disbelief.

Before them lay the semi-circle of buildings that was their future home. To the left, in gardens of its own, stood Government House, a two-storied stone building. There were few other large build-ings. The Military Barracks and the Hospital stood on the hill at the back of the township, with the Church to its right, and the orphanage in front, down near the water. There were a few large houses and stores belonging to wealthy individuals. Apart from this the township was made up of small, white-washed wattle-and-daub houses, while round to the extreme right, where the poor and destitute lived, was only a jumble of huts.

Bligh was not dismayed. To him, this was another challenge, and all his enthusiasm and energy were at hand to face it.

"We'll alter things, Mary," he said confidently. "We'll see a flourishing city before we're finished."

Nothing was lacking in the welcome given to the new Governor, by both the military and the lead-ing citizens. The soldiers turned out in their gayest colours, their red coats bright in the sun, the cannons booming. Bligh was given an address of welcome, and he and Mary had their first sight of John Macarthur, now no longer a captain, but an ordinary citizen, smiling, dark, arrogant and handsome. They also met Lieutenant-Colonel Johnston, the fair, weak-faced leader of the New

South Wales Corps, and other leading citizens, property owners, traders.

There were soon signs of the rift that lay beneath the happy welcome.

"Look, Mary," said Bligh one day, soon after their arrival. "I've received another address of welcome from the citizens of Sydney."

"But they gave you one when you arrived," objected Mary.

"Yes, I know," replied Bligh. "But d'you remember Macarthur signed it for the free settlers? This new address says he was the last person they would have chosen to sign for them. They say it's mainly due to him that the price of mutton is so high."

Soon after that, yet another address of welcome arrived. This one was from the free settlers of the Hawkesbury River. They were even stronger in their criticism of Macarthur and his friends.

"See what's here now, Mary," said Bligh to his daughter. "From the free settlers of the Hawkesbury. And you should hear what *they* think about the present system. Most bitter about the control the army people have over trade. They beg for the right to be able to sell their wheat at a fair price, and to get money for payment. No rum, they say, or useless goods."

"Surely that's fair enough."

"Indeed it is. But how terrible that people should have to beg to get fair payment for their goods."

"Do you think it's true, Papa? The people seem pleasant enough—and polite. No one could have been kinder to us than Mr. and Mrs. Macarthur. And the officers too. It's hard to believe they could be so heartless."

" I agree with you, Mary," replied Bligh, begining to pace excitedly up and down. " It is hard to believe. D'you know what I'm going to do? I'll make a complete tour of the Colony. I'll speak to every farmer I can find. On the Parramatta and on the Hawkesbury, I'll find out for myself exactly how things are."

BLIGH was appalled by what he found. With his usual thoroughness he toured the whole colony, visiting every farmhouse, big and small, and talking to each farmer. Along the Hawkesbury River, particularly, he found conditions very bad. Six months previously, a dreadful flood had swept down the river, and completely destroyed many of the farms. Wheat and flour became so short that some houses were without bread for months, and what bread there was was sold for five shillings a loaf. Bligh also found that everything he had heard about the rum trade and the army officers was true. The small people were being ruined to make money for the wealthy property owners.

Again, with his usual thoroughness and efficiency, he set about correcting the ills and evils he found.

He made arrangements for cattle from the Government herds to be killed and divided among the most needy. He arranged that farmers could get what goods they needed from the Government stores and pay for them after the next harvest—" everything from a needle to an anchor, from a pen'orth of pack thread to a ship's cable ", wrote one of Bligh's supporters. This, we feel, was probably an exaggeration. He arranged that a set price would be paid for wheat. He drew up a list of the public buildings that were in a bad state of repair, or not finished, and set convicts working on them.

Then, before the end of the year, he started the really far-reaching reforms. He issued an order that all purchases and payments were to be made in proper currency, and the use of spirits and other liquors as payment for grain, labour or any other goods was completely forbidden.

By the first Christmas, Bligh and his small band of supporters felt that good progress was being made.

" It's been a good start, Mary," he said. " In another year, with a good harvest, the colony should be on its feet again."

" The small settlers are tremendously grateful for all you've done," replied Mary. " Mr. Suttor was telling me yesterday that they cannot speak highly enough of you."

Little did Bligh and his daughter know that the traders and the officers were merely biding their time. Already they were at work in their own fashion to undermine his laws and authority.

At first, everything appeared to be going well. The Macarthurs and Lieutenant-Colonel Johnston and many other traders and army officers dined regularly at Government House. Balls and parties were held, and nothing of great importance upset the good relations of the small colony. The only shadow over the Bligh household, was the illness of John Putland, who had developed consumption, and was growing steadily weaker.

In February, however, Bligh had his first real brush with Macarthur. When Macarthur had returned from England with his grant for 5,000 acres, he had persuaded Governor King to approve it immediately. Not satisfied with the size of this grant he took it out in one of the best areas, an area not far from Sydney, which included the famous Cowpastures. These were large public lands where wild Government herds of cattle wandered and increased.

One morning, early in 1807, Macarthur called on Bligh to discuss the grant and to see if the Governor would give him government assistance in his sheep breeding. Bligh's anger at this man, who was trying to take land for his own use that the colony needed, suddenly overwhelmed him. A flow of tactless words poured from him.

"What have I to do with your sheep, sir?" he shouted. "What have I to do with your cattle? Are you to have such flocks and herds of cattle as no man ever heard of before? No, sir!"

"But," replied Macarthur, his arrogant face also dark with anger. "Don't forget that I've already been granted this land by an order from the Secretary of State, sir. In London, sir."

"I know, Mr. Macarthur!" shouted Bligh again. "I know! I have heard of your concerns, sir. You have got five thousand acres of land in the finest situation in the country. But you shan't keep it! No, you shan't keep it!"

Bligh had already written to England, pointing out that the land Macarthur had chosen was essential to the colony. It is important to note that Bligh was not questioning that Macarthur should have the grant. Though he did not approve of it, if the Secretary of State for the Colonies had given the grant to Macarthur, then Bligh would obey the instructions. He did, however, question its position. Cattle from the Cowpastures had been used when he first arrived to help the needy settlers after the dreadful floods. He knew from this very recent experience how essential this land was.

Everywhere he turned, stood Macarthur, with some plan or some proposal against the interests of the small people of the struggling settlement. Bligh was determined to fight him.

Macarthur for his part, slowly began to realize that Bligh would not allow things to go on as they were. Bligh, different from the last two governors, would enforce the laws and regulations he made.

From that time he began to use all his guile and cunning, his power over men, his cleverness in twisting things to suit his own use, his wealth and influence, to make the Governor's life impossible. In doing this he had the ready help of most of the army officers and unscrupulous settlers. who were in Australia to get what they could by any means.

One of the ways Macarthur and the army officers fought was to bring law actions against men who supported the Governors. The Criminal Courts were made up of Army officers, and the one man who should have been independent, the Judge Advocate, was a weak, vacillating drunkard. Though sometimes opposed to Macarthur he was utterly unreliable.

Bligh's opponents also used the law courts to introduce witnesses who would say critical or insulting things about the Governor. Although this evidence had nothing to do with the case, and should not have been allowed, the officers listened

F

to it. There was no wireless, or free newspapers, or elections, and what was said in the court quickly spread among the people.

There were many such cases. One famous example was about two stills for making alcohol that John Macarthur and Captain Abbot imported into the country. It was illegal to import such stills and illegal to make rum, so Bligh ordered that the stills should be returned to London. Macarthur, however, was allowed to have the large coppers, the main part of the stills, sent to his store so that other goods of his, packed in the coppers, could be taken out.

This played right into Macarthur's hand. He immediately twisted the situation so that Bligh was made to appear a tyrant in getting the coppers back from him. The naval officer, Robert Campbell, a staunch supporter of Bligh, sent his nephew to take back the stills. After much quibbling on Macarthur's part over receipts and authorities, young Robert Campbell seized the stills. Macarthur immediately brought a law case against him for illegal seizure of property. He said young Campbell did not have the proper authority.

This was a typical example of how Macarthur twisted every occurrence to harass the Government. The stills were illegal in the first place. Macarthur should never have imported them, and when they did arrive, should not have removed them to his property. Yet when they were taken back from him, *he* was the one who took the case to the courts and was able to make it appear as if he had been wronged. The case was given in his favour, and at the end he was allowed to make a fiery speech. Every British subject in the Colony, according to him, had no rights, and could have their goods seized at any time!

So the blackening of Bligh's name continued. Macarthur and his followers would so resist all his reforms that, in carrying them out, he was made to appear a tyrant and a despot. Added to this, it must be remembered that Bligh was never a tactful or patient man, so his opponents had many stories they could spread around the colony, exaggerate, and include in their letters home.

This battle of tactics continued right through 1807, and against this background, Bligh was trying to carry on his day-by-day administration, to care for the hundreds of orphan children of convict women, children who were left to wander the streets; to repair convict buildings; to help the small settlers; to send his despatches home. Also, over the entire struggle hung the shadow of his son-in-law, slowly dying with consumption.

On December 7, 1807, Bligh burst into the downstairs office, where Mary was talking to Griffin, the secretary.

"D'you know what he's done now?" shouted Bligh, waving his arms around and beginning to stride up and down the room. "D'you know what he's done?"

There was no need to ask about whom he was talking, and Bligh did not even wait for a reply.

"He's told the Captain of the *Parramatta* that he's not going to be responsible for feeding the crew any more. He's washed his hands of them."

"But it's Mr. Macarthur's ship, Papa," exclaimed Mary. "He can't just abandon the men."

"He's just trying to make trouble again, sir," said Griffin.

"Of course he is! Of course he is! The wretched man! D'you know what'll happen now? Those men will have to come ashore. They can't stay on the ship, with no food. They'll be forced to come ashore and then they'll break the law. And no doubt Macarthur'll spread it around that it's my fault they're not being fed."

There was a law in the country that if a convict escaped on board a ship, the owner of that ship had to pay an £800 bond. Some months previously, a dangerous convict named John Hoare had escaped on board Macarthur's ship, the *Parramatta*. When the ship returned to Sydney, Macarthur was ordered to pay the bond. In his usual manner he started writing letters, sending petitions, trying to confuse matters in order to avoid paying.

The Naval Officer, Robert Campbell, then seized the ship and placed two constables aboard. As the ship had thus not been cleared, the crew could not go ashore.

It was at this stage that Macarthur wrote to the Captain and crew, saying he would no longer be responsible for their pay or provisions. As Bligh had foreseen, the crew, after a week, were forced to leave the ship and come ashore, breaking the law.

The Judge Advocate, Atkins, sent a note to Macarthur asking him to come to Government House to explain his reasons for not feeding the crew. Macarthur refused. A constable was then sent to arrest him, on the charge "of illegally stopping the provisions of the master, mates and crew", of the schooner *Parramatta*, "thus compelling them to come unauthorized on shore".

It was this action that finally led to the last great clash between Bligh and Macarthur.

In Macarthur's eyes it was bad enough that Bligh should be questioning the positions of his land grants, depriving him and his friends of the enormous profits they made through selling rum, taking the free convict labour away from them— but that he should now have the effrontery to have him personally arrested, this was too much for the proud, wealthy John Macarthur.

In a fit of temper he resisted the arrest, and, sitting at his desk, wrote the following note to the police magistrate:

> Mr. Oakes,
> You will inform the persons who sent you here with the warrant you have now shown me and given me a copy of, that I never will submit to the horrid tyranny that is attempted, until I am forced; that I consider it with scorn and contempt, as I do the persons who have directed it to be executed.
>
> J. Macarthur.

He had now put himself completely in the wrong. He had acted illegally in refusing to pay the £800 bond and in refusing to feed his crew. He was now openly rebelling against the Government and expressing scorn and contempt for His Majesty's representatives. There was ample evidence against him, and Bligh ordered his arrest. On December 17 he was committed for trial on a number of charges—importing illicit stills, disturbing the peace, inflaming the minds of the people against the Governor, causing the seamen of the *Parramatta* to break the law, and using seditious words and threats against the King's Government and Governor. The trial was to take place at the next Criminal Court, which would be held on January 25 of the next year.

Macarthur had to be let out on bail, and he at once started to scheme and plot. He had six weeks to work his supporters up to the point where they would rid themselves of Bligh. It would appear he had now realized that if John Macarthur were to stay in the Colony, then Governor Bligh must go.

IN a tense atmosphere, the trial opened on the morning of January 25, 1808. The hot, steaming courtroom was packed with civilians and soldiers, excited, sweating, expectant. For weeks the intrigues and plots had continued. Macarthur had been visiting, talking, accusing, stirring up trouble, laying the foundations for the climax he could foresee.

He had sent a stream of letters to Bligh, objecting to Atkins sitting in the court. Atkins, he said, owed him money and was therefore an interested party. He had obtained an old promissory note of Atkins, saying he owed someone else £26. It was fourteen years old, so, with interest, was now worth £82. It would be unfair, said Macarthur, for a man who owed him money to sit as Judge Advocate at his trial. Once again Macarthur made himself appear unjustly treated.

He also started to fence in the land for which he held a lease near the church. This was a lease about which Bligh had already written home. He realized it was against public interest for Macarthur to lease this land. There was a public well on it, and when Macarthur started to fence it in, Bligh immediately insisted he must wait until a decision came from England. Macarthur continued to fence it in. Bligh had him forcibly stopped, and once more Macarthur could go around, acting the injured innocent.

The final step in the plotting took place the night before the trial. A large regimental dinner was held, behind locked doors, with drink flowing freely and the band playing. The officers and their friends were there, though Macarthur made a point of being absent, and doubtless any wavering or dissenting voices would be stilled under the comradeship of eating and drinking.

So the trial opened.

The six army officers, who were to make up the court, were sworn in. Then came the turn of Atkins, Judge Advocate, who had also to be sworn in. Immediately Macarthur was on his feet. Atkins, he said, was his enemy, and it would be against British justice to be tried by his enemy. It was certainly against British justice to be tried by six of your friends, but there was no one to point that out. Instead, the six army officers allowed Macarthur to read a long and insulting speech against Atkins, giving the impression, among other things, that Macarthur's life, honour and property were all threatened.

Every time Atkins tried to speak, he was howled down. Finally, afraid for *his* life, the poor man left the court, leaving the floor to the Macarthur faction.

All this time, Bligh was at Government House, in the company of the few loyal civilian magistrates and friends, wondering what was happening, waiting for news. Then there came a note from the six army officers saying they could not continue the trial without a Judge Advocate, and demanding that a new one be appointed.

Bligh replied that it was not within his power to appoint a new one.

All day the argument continued, with notes flying from the courtroom to Government House. The army officers refused to continue without a new Judge Advocate, but Bligh maintained that Atkins must remain in that position. Bligh then appealed to Lieutenant-Colonel Johnston to discipline his officers, and make them carry out the laws of the colony. But Johnston, many miles away at his house in Annandale, sent word he was too ill to take part. He said he had hurt himself falling out of his carriage coming home from the dinner the night before. Rumour had it that he was extremely drunk. In any case, he was not badly hurt, and it was obvious that he was prepared to support the officers in their defiance of the Governor.

"What can I do?" asked Bligh desperately, pacing up and down the verandah of Government House. "How can I make them act?" With him were his few supporters, men who were prepared to stand with him against the Military.

"Order the officers to come here and explain their actions," suggested Campbell.

Next day, when the officers again refused to carry on the trial, they were summoned to Government House. This they had no intention of doing, and went, instead, to the barracks. Now Macarthur had the situation in the palm of his hand, exactly as he had planned it.

The six army officers had defied the Governor, and now only open rebellion would save them too from arrest and trial.

All day rumours were spread around the colony. Bligh's enemies said that he was going to do away with the courts of justice. Drink was given out freely, and the malcontents in the streets of Sydney were ready for action. The leaders of the rebels collected at the Barracks, and at five o'clock Lieutenant-Colonel Johnson, who had been too sick to take action for Bligh the night before, joined them. There were not many of them, possibly only about a dozen, but they were very vocal. A terrible picture was painted. If Bligh were not arrested, they said, there would be a massacre, bloodshed, rebellion, the people in Sydney would rise up against the Governor. Johnston was easily convinced. He made no attempt to call at Government House and find out from Bligh the real truth of the position. Instead, he sent an order for Macarthur to be released from gaol.

As soon as Macarthur reached the Barracks he joined his voice to those of the army officers whom Bligh had prevented from growing as rich as they thought they should. The colony was in "an alarming state" they said, and "every man's property, liberty and life" were endangered. It was certainly not Bligh who had brought the colony to this alarming state. The only people who were threatening the peace of the colony, the true course of justice, and the "property, liberty and life" of the average man, were John Macarthur and his friends.

But they won the day.

Johnston gave the order for the officers to assemble the soldiers. At about half-past six, while it was still broad daylight, the regiment was formed up on the parade ground in front of the barracks, and, with Johnston at its head, and with colours

flying and the band playing "The British Grena-
diers", they marched with a quick step towards
Government House.

At Government House Atkins was the first to
realize what was happening. He had dined with
Bligh and had then left to find what news he could
from the town. He returned panic stricken, pale
and shaking.

"There is a great movement in Barrack Square,"
gasped. "The Military are under arms."

"You don't mean they would attack me in person?" asked Bligh. That these malcontents would
physically attack his person, and his position as the
King's Representative, had never occurred to him.
"I can't believe it," was all he said.

Mary then went out to see if what Atkins said
was correct, and she too came rushing in.
"They're marching towards us, Papa," she cried.
"They're nearly here."

Still Bligh was silent and motionless, white with
anger.

"What will you do, Papa?" she cried, amazed
at her father's inaction.

But suddenly he found his tongue. "I must
escape," he said, slowly and deliberately. "I must
try and reach the Hawkesbury. Perhaps I can find
support there. And my papers! Griffin! We
must try and save my private papers. They will
be my only defence with the Government at
home." Bligh realized at once how important his
papers would be in the judging of the situation at
a later date.

"I'll try and stop them," cried Mary, "while
you escape."

Before anyone could prevent her she had run down to the gate of Government House, and for a few moments she delayed the advance of the valiant New South Wales Corps—three hundred and fifty men, all fully armed and coming to arrest one man. But she was soon thrust aside, and in five minutes Government House was surrounded and the men with Bligh arrested. It took longer to find Bligh, for he was in a small upstairs room, hiding papers on his person, and hoping for a chance to escape. But he too was soon discovered and put under arrest.

Thus ended his valiant attempt to fight, single-handed, the strength of the army officers and the wealthy citizens, and to establish a free, good life for the small man.

After Bligh's arrest, control of the colony went back into the hands of the army and all the abuses of their earlier rule started again. The men who had stood by Bligh suffered grievously. They were imprisoned, punished, and lost their property. The rebels and their friends were once again given large grants of land, free labour, monopoly of rum and trading.

And, once again, the blackening of Bligh's name began. The only way the rebels could in any way justify their actions was to prove to the Government at home that Bligh had been a tyrant, a bully, a despot. False stories were invented, false reports were sent home to England. He was accused of interfering with justice and of using Government stores for his own use. He was even said to be a coward and to have been found hiding under a bed at Government House. To call Bligh a coward

was one of the most ridiculous things ever said
about him.   His whole career, every single event
in it, shows him as a man of courage and action,
always willing to stand doggedly by what he
thought was right.

Again, as with the mutiny of the *Bounty*, many
of the malicious things said about him have been
repeated in the history books.   Many of the people
who wrote these history books were friends or,
later on, descendants of the men who deprived
Bligh of his true position.   It suited them to
repeat the falsehoods.   So, once again, we find
Bligh misrepresented for future generations.

If the history books have wronged him, however,
the authorities in England were not misled.   At
the time, they fully realized that Bligh was in the
right, and Macarthur and Johnston in the wrong.
All the false reports, the lies, the malicious stories,
could not hide the truth.   When the shouting and
the tumult died, there were plenty of honest,
reliable witnesses who were willing to write long
letters home, or even travel back to England themselves, to stand by the Governor who had tried to
abolish the many abuses in the colony, and to give
evidence of all the good things he tried to introduce.

So if Bligh himself was defeated by the rebels,
what he fought for was upheld.   Moreover, the
very fact of his arrest made the Government at
home realize two very important things—firstly,
that no real progress could be made in Australia,
while the New South Wales Corps was there, and
secondly, that the courts must be reformed.

So, on December 28, 1809, nearly two years after

Bligh's overthrow, Governor Macquarie, accompanied by two warships, arrived at Sydney.

This was the end of the rebel government. Macquarie had instructions to re-instate Bligh for one day, so that the colonists would know that Bligh had the support and approval of the Government at home. Even more important than that, Macquarie brought with him a new regiment of troops, under proper discipline. The men punished by the rebel government were immediately restored to their positions and property, the grants made by the rebel government were cancelled. One cannot say that Macquarie's rule was completely successful. He tried to conciliate the opposition and allowed many of the people who had contributed towards Bligh's downfall to go unscathed. He was, however, able to bring about reforms with a strong hand, and from this time the small colony began truly to develop. Fine buildings appeared, trade was re-organized, the courts functioned more fairly. With a strong, stable Government men went forth and discovered new country, and the Government surveyed and controlled it.

Bligh returned home to a further honourable career. In 1811 the court-martial of Johnston was held, and Bligh's actions were upheld. Johnston was found guilty and cashiered from the army. As for Macarthur, he, as usual, manipulated things to save his own skin. He left New South Wales for England before Macquarie arrived with instructions to arrest him. Because Macarthur was a civilian he could not be tried in England, and as long as he stayed in England, he was safe. This meant he spent nine bitter years in exile, all the time longing to return to Australia.

In England, after the court-martial, Bligh was promoted Rear-Admiral of the Blue Squadron, then in 1812, he was made Rear-Admiral of the White. He was again received at court, and was paid his full pension as ex-Governor of New South Wales.

His had been a stormy career, stormy because he did not know the meaning of the word compromise, and because, whatever the odds, he stood bravely for what he thought was right. A sense of duty, a great courage, and the ability to hold out in face of seemingly impossible obstacles, would seldom be found in greater strength than in the character of William Bligh.